QUICK MENTAL MATHS

MENTAL RECALL PRACTICE FOR 7 YEAR OLDS

SCHOLASTIC MATHS SKILLS

G000042984

AUTHOR
William Hartley

DESIGNER
Mark Udall

EDITOR
Kate Pearce

ILLUSTRATIONS
George Turner

ASSISTANT EDITOR
Claire Miller

COVER ARTWORK
James Alexander/
David Oliver
(Berkeley
Studios)

SERIES DESIGNER
Anna Oliwa

Text © 1999 William Hartley
© 1999 Scholastic Ltd

Designed using Adobe Pagemaker
Published by Scholastic Ltd, Villiers House, Clarendon
Avenue, Leamington Spa, Warwickshire CV32 5PR

1234567890   9012345678

British Library Cataloguing-in-Publication Data
A catalogue record for this book is available from the
British Library.

ISBN 0-590-53919-1

The right of William Hartley to be identified as the Author of this
Work has been asserted by him in accordance with the Copyright,
Designs and Patents Act 1988.

SEC	SHEET	SHEET HEADING	SUGGESTED ORAL MATHS INPUT
COUNTING AND ORDERING	A1	COUNTING IN STEPS	Count on/back in 2s, 3s, 4s and 5s to 50 and 10s to 100.
	A2	PLACE VALUE	What do the 1, the 3 and the 5 in 135 mean? See B11 and C11.
	A3	ORDERING WHOLE NUMBERS AND FRACTIONS	Order numbers up to 50. Order the fractions ½ ¼ ⅓.
	A4	ESTIMATING AND APPROXIMATING	Estimate groups of objects up to 50.
	A5	ROUNDING	Round any two-digit number to the nearest 10.
	A6	TEST YOUR SKILLS 1 (A1–A3 REVIEW SHEET)	As for A1–A3.
	A7	TEST YOUR SKILLS 2 (A4–A5 REVIEW SHEET)	As for A4 and A5.
ADDITION AND SUBTRACTION	B1	ADDITION FACTS	Addition facts to 10 + 10.
	B2	SUBTRACTION FACTS	Subtraction problems with numbers less than 20.
	B3	RELATIONSHIP BETWEEN + AND –	Problems like: 17 + 11, 11 + 17, 28 – 11, 28 – 17.
	B4	PAIRS AND DOUBLES	Pairs to 10. Doubles to 20 + 20, plus 10s to 100 + 100.
	B5	ADDING ORDER	TU numbers (no bridging). Putting the larger number first.
	B6	IDENTIFYING NEAR DOUBLES	Problems like: 7 + 8 = 15 because 7 + 7 = 14 plus 1 = 15.
	B7	CALCULATION PATTERNS (+ AND –)	Problems like: 2 + 5 = 7, 12 + 5 = 17, 22 + 5 = 27, and so on.
	B8	PARTITIONING AND RECOMBINING	Partition into 5s and a bit to add amounts below 30.
	B9	BRIDGING AND ADJUSTING	Problems like: 16 + 8 = 16 + 4 + 4 = 20 + 4 = 24.
	B10	+ AND – WHOLE NUMBERS AND FRACTIONS	Two-digit to/from two-digit number with no bridging.
	B11	PLACE VALUE WHEN ADDING AND SUBTRACTING	Meaning of 'units', 'tens' and 'hundreds'. See A2 and C11.
	B12	ADDING AND SUBTRACTING SEVERAL NUMBERS	Adding/subtracting three numbers and crossing the 10s.
	B13	TEST YOUR SKILLS 1 (B1–B6 REVIEW SHEET)	As for B1–B6.
	B14	TEST YOUR SKILLS 2 (B7–B12 REVIEW SHEET)	As for B7–B12.
MULTIPLICATION AND DIVISION	C1	MULTIPLICATION FACTS	On and back in 2s to 20, 5s to 50 and 10s to 100.
	C2	DIVISION FACTS	Division facts for 2, 5 and 10 times tables.
	C3	RELATIONSHIP BETWEEN × AND ÷	Ask for the missing fact: 2 × 5 = 10, 5 × 2 = 10, 10 ÷ 2 = 5, ?
	C4	DOUBLES AND HALVES	All numbers to 10. Multiples of 10 as far as 100.
	C5	MULTIPLICATION ORDER	Reinforce 'multiplication can be done in any order'.
	C6	DIVISION WITH REMAINDERS	Reinforce the meaning of 'left over' and 'remainder'.
	C7	CALCULATION PATTERNS (× AND ÷)	Look for × and ÷ patterns in the 2, 5 and 10 times tables.
	C8	MULTIPLYING BY 1, 10	Problems like: 10 × 5, 2 × 10, 10 × 10.
	C9	DIVIDING BY 1, 10	Problems like: 30 ÷ 10, 80 ÷ 10.
	C10	MORE MULTIPLICATION FACTS	Practice multiplying multiples of 10 by 2, 5 and 10.
	C11	PLACE VALUE WHEN MULTIPLYING AND DIVIDING	Problems like: 1H + 3T + 6U equals? See A2 and B11.
	C12	× AND ÷ WHOLE NUMBERS AND FRACTIONS	Practice × and ÷ facts for the 2, 5 and 10 times table.
	C13	TEST YOUR SKILLS 1 (C1–C6 REVIEW SHEET)	As for C1–C6.
	C14	TEST YOUR SKILLS 2 (C7–C12 REVIEW SHEET)	As for C7–C12.
MULTISTEP AND MIXED OPERATIONS	D1	ADDING AND SUBTRACTING	Choose any addition and subtraction activities.
	D2	MULTIPLYING AND DIVIDING	Choose any multiplication and division activities.
	D3	ADDING AND MULTIPLYING	Choose any addition and multiplication activities.
	D4	SUBTRACTING AND DIVIDING	Choose any subtraction and division activities.

ABOUT THE SERIES

Quick Mental Maths aims to help children develop quick mental recall strategies – both the instant recall of known facts and speedy methods of figuring out 'unknowns'. Number facts are the vital building blocks for calculation, and their easy access is the key to efficient, accurate and confident mental mathematical ability.

Quick Mental Maths is a series of six photocopiable books providing a mixture of problem-posing styles of mental number practice for children aged 6 to 11. The level of ability at which each book is pitched has been broadly determined from the recommendations of the National Numeracy *Framework* document. *Quick Mental Maths* can be used as an independent resource in its own right to support any of the UK curriculum documentation, but can also be used in conjunction with the other Scholastic series *Developing Mental Maths* and *Practising Mental Maths*.

The books will provide valuable reinforcement of number bonds and times tables and help to improve the children's mental agility, as well as consolidating and extending their knowledge and use of mathematical vocabulary. These worksheets could be used as regular number practice – perhaps with a short time allowed each day for the children to complete one or more sections of a worksheet – as pre-SATs reinforcement/assessment tasks, or as worthwhile homework pages. All photocopiable sheets are indicated by the icon ⓟ.

ABOUT THE BOOK STRUCTURE
IN-BUILT DIFFERENTIATION

Each of the six books in this series addresses the same mental maths content under the same worksheet heading in each book, but at an increasing level of complexity. Thus, for example, you will find that worksheet A2 is always 'Place value' and worksheet C6 is always about 'Division with remainders'. Therefore, differentiation in a mixed-ability class is made easy by using the same worksheet number from more than one book to provide the same material at different levels.

YOUR INPUT

In order to reinforce the intended strategy to be used by the children to complete each sheet, it is recommended that you engage in some oral maths work with the class before they start. A varied use of mathematical vocabulary is very important when doing this. Some brief guidance for this aspect of your lesson preparation is given alongside each worksheet heading on the 'Teacher's information chart' on the opposite page. (You will find other suitable oral maths activities described in detail in the Scholastic teachers' book *Developing Mental Maths with 5–7 year olds*.)

RECORD-KEEPING

The photocopiable record sheet on the next page is to facilitate your record-keeping and assessment. This can either be given to the child as a record of his or her achievement or used as a teacher's record of which pages have been completed by which children and with what degree of success.

CONTENT ORGANIZATION

Each book is split into four sections:
A Counting and ordering
B Addition and subtraction
C Multiplication and division
D Multistep and mixed operations

The activities on each worksheet in sections A–C concentrate on one strategy, offering instant recall practice, number and word problems and a more investigational extension activity. The intention is that the page represents an 'achievable minimum' for children working at that level and that the extension activity (indicated by the icon 🖎) will only be attempted by the more able child using a separate maths book or on blank paper which can then be included in his or her personal maths file. In this way, it is hoped that the less able child will be able to tackle the majority of the page, while the more able child also has a 'special challenge'.

At the end of each of the first three sections (A–C) you will find two review tests relating specifically to the content of the sheets in that section. The problems are numbered to key in with the worksheet pages to which the questions relate. These review sheets will provide you with an opportunity to assess how well each child is progressing with the strategies on the worksheets in that section.

The final section of worksheets (D) gives the children the chance to practise some of their developing skills using more involved mental operation sequences that often require them to hold on to an interim number. The sheets in this section will really challenge the children.

ANSWERS

The final pages of the book provide the answers to all, but the most open-ended, of the questions on each worksheet. Answers in bold indicate those numbers which are given on the worksheets.

ABOUT THIS BOOK

Quick Mental Maths for 7 year olds is intended for Year 2/P3 children working at NC/NIC Level 2 (NNP Year 2) or confidently within Scottish Level B. It is hoped the activities in this book will help to reinforce the children's knowledge and understanding of place value, counting and 2, 5 and 10 times tables, and that it will lead children into adopting some of the many different strategies and techniques available to them for tackling daily mathematical situations with confidence and efficiency.

RECORD SHEET

SHEET NO	MARK	COMMENT
A1		
A2		
A3		
A4		
A5		
A6		
A7		
B1		
B2		
B3		
B4		
B5		
B6		
B7		
B8		
B9		
B10		
B11		
B12		
B13		
B14		

SHEET NO	MARK	COMMENT
C1		
C2		
C3		
C4		
C5		
C6		
C7		
C8		
C9		
C10		
C11		
C12		
C13		
C14		
D1		
D2		
D3		
D4		

COUNTING IN STEPS

A1

1. Put in the missing numbers.

a. 8p 10p [   ] 14p [   ] 18p [   ] [   ] 24p

b. ⬠ 27 24 ⬠ ⬠ 15 ⬠ 9 ⬠

2a. Count on in 4s from 4. Colour each number you land on red.

4	5	6	7	8
9	10	11	12	13
14	15	16	17	18
19	20	21	22	23
24	25	26	27	28

2b. Count on in 5s from 5. Colour each number you land on blue.

5	6	7	8	9	10
11	12	13	14	15	16
17	18	19	20	21	22
23	24	25	26	27	28
29	30	31	32	33	34
35	36	37	38	39	40

3. Write in the missing words.

zero [   ] twenty [   ] forty

[   ] [   ] [   ]

eighty [   ] one hundred

 Write from 2–100 in 2s, 3–99 in 3s, 4–100 in 4s and 5–100 in 5s.

COUNTING AND ORDERING

COUNTING AND ORDERING

PLACE VALUE

1. Put the right numbers in the boxes. Like this: 12 = 10 + 2.

a. 29 = ☐ + 9

f. 46 = ☐ + 6

b. 18 = 10 + ☐

g. 30 + 3 = ☐

c. ☐ = 50 + 5

h. ☐ = 15 + 4

d. 37 = ☐ + 7

i. 42 = ☐ + 2

e. 21 = 20 + ☐

j. 17 = 10 + ☐

2. How many 10p coins and 1p coins would you need for:

a. fifty-four pence? ☐ 10p coins and ☐ 1p coins

b. sixty-seven pence? ☐ 10p coins and ☐ 1p coins

c. seventy-two pence? ☐ 10p coins and ☐ 1p coins

3. Answer these questions.

a. How many is the digit 3 in forty-three worth? ☐

b. What does the 7 stand for in seventy-five? ☐

c. How much is the digit 1 in 129 worth? ☐

Draw some abacuses and show these numbers on them:
101, 230, 847, 406, 640, 46, 538, 358, 853, 770.

ORDERING WHOLE NUMBERS AND FRACTIONS

1a. Put these weights in order, starting with the smallest.

31kg	22kg	50kg	43kg	14kg	45kg

b. Put these lengths in order, starting with the longest.

33cm	16cm	41cm	17cm	49cm	20cm

2. Make the numbers in the middle boxes 2 less and then 3 more. The first one has been done for you.

− 2	a.	+ 3	− 2	b.	+ 3	− 2	c.	+ 3
23	25	28		19			11	
	38			44			8	
	31			27			40	

3. Shade in half of shape a, a third of shape b and a quarter of shape c.

a.

b.

c.

 Make up some number blocks of your own like those in part 2.

COUNTING AND ORDERING

ESTIMATING AND APPROXIMATING

COUNTING AND ORDERING

1. Using the number line, work out which number each animal is standing on.

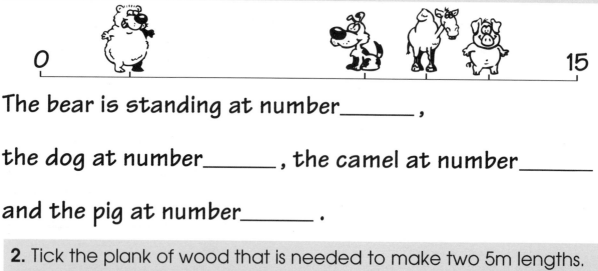

0   15

The bear is standing at number_____ ,

the dog at number_____ , the camel at number_____

and the pig at number_____ .

2. Tick the plank of wood that is needed to make two 5m lengths. Then colour the longest plank red, the shortest plank blue and the other plank green.

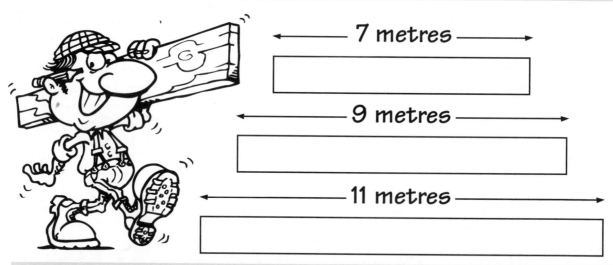

←——— 7 metres ———→

←——— 9 metres ———→

←——— 11 metres ———→

3. Guess how many paces it would take to get across your classroom, then pace it out.

I thought it was [ ] paces. It was actually [ ] paces.

Work with a friend and take it in turns to estimate halves, thirds and quarters of numbers. Set a time-limit for your answers and keep a score.

ROUNDING

1. Round these lengths to the nearest 10cm.

14cm   96cm   27cm   54cm   38cm   65cm

☐   ☐   ☐   ☐   ☐   ☐

2. Give the answers to these problems, then round the answers to the nearest 10. The first one has been done for you.

a. 14 + 24 = 38 | 40   f. 39 – 6 = ☐ ☐

b. 23 – 12 = ☐ ☐   g. 15 + 15 = ☐ ☐

c. 17 + 51 = ☐ ☐   h. 78 – 33 = ☐ ☐

d. 29 – 8 = ☐ ☐   i. 21 + 22 = ☐ ☐

e. 9 + 9 = ☐ ☐   j. 37 – 6 = ☐ ☐

3. Fill in the missing numbers. The first one has been done for you.

a. The nearest 10 to 66 is [70]

b. Forty-five is half-way between ☐ and [50]

c. 53p is closer to ☐ than to [60p]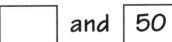

d. 5 minutes to 9 is nearer to ☐

    than to [8 o'clock]

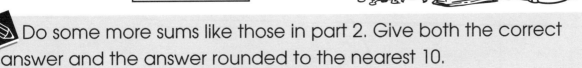 Do some more sums like those in part 2. Give both the correct answer and the answer rounded to the nearest 10.

QUICK MENTAL MATHS

TEST YOUR SKILLS 1 (A1–A3)

A1 Put in the missing numbers.

a. 12p   15p   [   ]   21p   [   ]   27p   [   ]

b. ⬡ 24m ⬡ 16m ⬡ 8m ⬡

[ ]

A2 Answer these questions.

a. How many is the digit 4 in 34 worth? [   ]

b. What does the digit 2 in 29 stand for? [   ]

c. How much is the digit 1 in 150 worth? [   ]

[ ]

Write the correct numbers in the boxes.

d. 36 = [   ] + 6

e. 27 = 20 + [   ]

f. 45 = [   ] + 5

g. [   ] = 50 + 3

[ ]

A3 Shade in a half.   Shade in a quarter.

a. [   ]   b. [   ]

[ ]

Put these weights in order, starting with the smallest.

c. 27kg   53kg   14kg   36kg   49kg

[   ] [   ] [   ] [   ] [   ]

[ ]

TEST YOUR SKILLS 2 (A4–A5)

A4 Write a number that is close to:

a. 19 _____ 51 _____ 82 _____ 48 _____ 97 _____ ☐

Write a number that is nearly:

b. one hundred _____ sixty _____ thirty-five _____ ☐

Write in the boxes the numbers that should be at a, b, c and d.

c.

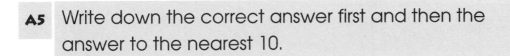

0   a   b c   d   14

☐ ☐ ☐ ☐ ☐

A5 Write down the correct answer first and then the answer to the nearest 10.

a. Fifteen add twenty-three. ☐ ☐

b. Thirty-seven take away fourteen. ☐ ☐

c. $8 + 7 =$ ☐ ☐   e. $20 - 3 =$ ☐ ☐

d. $19 - 6 =$ ☐ ☐   f. $9 + 9 =$ ☐ ☐ ☐

Fill in the missing time.

g. 10 past nine is nearer to ☐

than to 10 o'clock ☐

P

QUICK MENTAL MATHS

☐ TOTAL

ADDITION FACTS

1. Find the missing amounts.

a. $5kg + 5kg = \boxed{}$

f. $3p + \boxed{} = 7p$

b. $3p + 3p = \boxed{}$

g. $\boxed{} + 3cm = 9cm$

c. $8cm + 8cm = \boxed{}$

h. $3m + 5m = \boxed{}$

d. $6p + 6p = \boxed{}$

i. $2kg + \boxed{} = 6kg$

e. $9m + 9m = \boxed{}$

j. $\boxed{} + 2g = 5g$

2. Write in how many you need to add to each number to make 20. Like this: ten $\boxed{10}$

a. nine $\boxed{11}$ three $\boxed{}$ eight $\boxed{}$ six $\boxed{}$

b. five $\boxed{}$ twelve $\boxed{}$ four $\boxed{}$ one $\boxed{}$

c. two $\boxed{}$ eighteen $\boxed{}$ seven $\boxed{}$ fourteen $\boxed{}$

3. Answer the questions below, using the number line.

0 1 2 3 4 5 6 7 8 9 10 11 12 13 14 15

a. How many steps is it from 5 to 12? $\boxed{}$

b. How many steps is it from 4 to 15? $\boxed{}$

Write down as many pairs of numbers as you can think of that add up to 30.

QUICK MENTAL MATHS

SUBTRACTION FACTS

1. Fill in the missing numbers and signs in these sets.

					→				
a.	9	–		=	9	→	9	–	9		0
b.		–	1	=	8	→	9	–		=	1
c.	9	–	2	=		→	9		7	=	2
d.	9	–	3		6	→		–	6	=	3
e.	9		4	=	5	→	9	–	5	=	

2. Fill in the blanks.

a. ☐ – ☐ = 6   **d.** ☐ – ☐ = 5

b. ☐ – ☐ = 4   **e.** ☐ – ☐ = 8

c. ☐ – ☐ = 9   **f.** ☐ – ☐ = 7

3. Answer these questions.

a. What is 14 take away 7? ☐

b. What is six fewer than sixteen? ☐

c. From fifteen subtract eight. ☐

d. How many is twenty-four minus twelve? ☐

Write some sets of subtraction problems like the ones at the top of the page. Use the numbers 6, 7 and 8.

RELATIONSHIP BETWEEN + AND –

1. Fill in the missing amounts in these two sets.

a. $14cm + 5cm = \boxed{}$

$\boxed{} + 14cm = 19cm$

$19cm - \boxed{} = 5cm$

$19cm - 5cm = \boxed{}$

b. $11p + 7p = \boxed{}$

$\boxed{} + 11p = 18p$

$18p - \boxed{} = 7p$

$18p - 7p = \boxed{}$

c. What do you notice about each set?

_____

2. Now do the same with these harder number sentences.

a. $17m + 12m = \boxed{}$

$\boxed{} + 17m = 29m$

$29m - \boxed{} = 17m$

$29m - 17m = \boxed{}$

b. $30g + 50g = \boxed{}$

$\boxed{} + 30g = 80g$

$80g - \boxed{} = 50g$

$80g - 50g = \boxed{}$

3. Write in the missing number sentence.

$28 = 15 + 13, \quad 28 = 13 + 15, \quad 28 - 15 = 13,$ _____

Make up your own set of four number sentences using three two-digit numbers (like the ones shown in part 2).

QUICK MENTAL MATHS

PAIRS AND DOUBLES

1a. Write down pairs of numbers that add up to 8. One has been done for you.

7 + 1 _____

b. Now write down pairs of numbers that add up to 10.

_____

_____

2. Double these numbers.

a. 9 ☐   10 ☐   11 ☐   12 ☐

b. 13 ☐   14 ☐   15 ☐   20 ☐

c. 25 ☐   30 ☐   40 ☐   50 ☐

3. Use words to answer these questions.

a. Harry has 8p. Samina has twice as much. How much does Samina have? _____

b. A rubber costs 7p. What will be the cost of two rubbers? _____

c. How many do you have if you have double five? _____

Choose some numbers between 11 and 20 and write out all the number pairs that make those numbers.

QUICK MENTAL MATHS

ADDING ORDER

1. Rewrite these sums so that the bigger number comes first (like in the first sum). Then work them out.

a. 5 + 13 = 13 + 5 = 18   f. 3 + 17 = _____ = ____

b. 8 + 11 = _____ = ____   g. 5 + 12 = _____ = ____

c. 3 + 16 = _____ = ____   h. 6 + 14 = _____ = ____

d. 7 + 12 = _____ = ____   i. 6 + 11 = _____ = ____

e. 4 + 14 = _____ = ____   j. 3 + 15 = _____ = ____

2. Use each number once to make six sums. Put the larger number first each time. Find all the answers.

___ + ___ = ___   11 41 23 32   ___ + ___ = ___

___ + ___ = ___   21 34 43 31   ___ + ___ = ___

___ + ___ = ___   44 13 42 22   ___ + ___ = ___

3. Add 9 to each of these numbers.
Think about putting the larger number first.

five [ ]   seven [ ]   twelve [ ]   eighteen [ ]
+9   +9   +9   +9

Make up some of your own add sums using two, three or four numbers. Remember to write the numbers in order with the largest number first.

IDENTIFYING NEAR DOUBLES

1. Work out these sums by using doubles that you know.

a.	6	+	7	=		f.	15	+	14	=
b.	9	+	8	=		g.	11	+	12	=
c.	12	+	13	=		h.	18	+	17	=
d.	16	+	15	=		i.	10	+	11	=
e.	19	+	20	=		j.	9	+	10	=

2. Fill in the spaces. Use near doubles to help you.

a. $8 - 3 = 8 - 4 + 1 = \underline{\quad}$ d. $14 - 8 = 14 - 7 - 1 = \underline{\quad}$

b. $6 - 2 = \underline{\qquad\qquad} = 4$ e. $40 - 21 = \underline{\qquad\qquad} = 19$

c. $12 - 5 = 12 - 6 + 1 = \underline{\quad}$ f. $16 - 9 = 16 - 8 - 1 = \underline{\quad}$

3. Answer these questions. Use doubles to help you.

a. What is the total of forty and forty-one?

b. Twenty-nine plus thirty is equal to how many?

c. What is twenty-five add on twenty-six?

d. Which number is six less than fourteen?

 Add together other pairs of numbers that are 1 or 2 more or less than each other.

ADDITION AND SUBTRACTION

CALCULATION PATTERNS (+ AND –)

1. Fill in this square and then use it to work out the sums.

+	6	7	8	9	10
6	12			15	
7		14			
8					
9			17		
10					20

a. 6 + 10 = ☐

b. 7 + ☐ = 16

c. ☐ + 8 = 16

d. 9 + 7 = ☐

e. 10 + ☐ = 16

2a. Shade all the same numbers in the square in the same colour.

b. What do you notice about the number patterns in the square?

_____

_____

3. Finish off these patterns of numbers.

a. 8 – 5 = 3

18 – 5 = ____

28 – 5 = ____

68 – 5 = ____

b. 4 + 3 = 7

14 + 3 = ____

24 + 3 = ____

84 + 3 = ____

c. 9 – 4 = 5

19 – 4 = ____

49 – 4 = ____

99 – 4 = ____

Draw an add square like the one in part 1. Write the numbers 11 to 15 across the top and down the sides. Fill in the squares.

QUICK MENTAL MATHS

PARTITIONING AND RECOMBINING

1. The sum below shows my *thinking stages* for getting the answer.

18 + 7 = 15 + 3 + 5 + 2 = 15 + 5 + 3 + 2 = 20 + 5 = 25

Write out all your *thinking stages* when you do these two sums.

a. 16 + 8 = _____

_____

b. 17 + 8 = _____

_____

2. Do these sums. Try to think in the same way as you did in part 1.

a. 17kg + 9kg = _____

b. 7p + 16p = _____

c. 18cm + 8cm = _____

d. 6p + 17p = _____

e. 9m + 16m = _____

f. 26cm + 8cm = _____

g. 9m + 27m = _____

h. 28kg + 7kg = _____

i. 8p + 29p = _____

j. 6p + 27p = _____

3. Do this problem and give the answer in words.

Add together twenty-seven and eight. ┌──────────┐
                                      │   │
                                      └──────────┘

 Break down some hundreds, tens and units numbers into tens, fives and ones.

BRIDGING AND ADJUSTING

1. Work out the answer to this sum.

a. $8 + 7 = 8 + 2 + 5 = 10 + 5 = $ ☐

Now think in the same way to do these sums.

b. $9 + 8 = $ ☐   **e.** $3 + 8 = $ ☐   **h.** $7 + 6 = $ ☐

c. $6 + 9 = $ ☐   **f.** $7 + 4 = $ ☐   **i.** $8 + 4 = $ ☐

d. $8 + 6 = $ ☐   **g.** $6 + 7 = $ ☐   **j.** $9 + 7 = $ ☐

2. Work out the answer to this problem.

a. $15 - 9 = 15 - 5 - 4 = 10 - 4 = $ ☐

Think in the same way to do these problems.

b. $13 - 5 = $ ☐   **d.** $14 - 7 = $ ☐   **f.** $17 - 7 = $ ☐

c. $15 - 8 = $ ☐   **e.** $16 - 9 = $ ☐   **g.** $18 - 9 = $ ☐

3. Fill in the missing bits.

a. $17 + 8 = 17 + 3 + 5 = 20 + 5 = $ ____

b. $23 - 8 = 23 - 3 - 5 = $ _____ $= $ ____

c. $25 - 9 = $ _____ $= $ _____ $= $ ____

Write out in full your thinking stages for sums b-d of part 1 and problems b and c of part 2. (Look at part a in each one.)

+ AND – WHOLE NUMBERS AND FRACTIONS

1. Fill in these charts. Some of the answers have been put in already.

+	10	13	30	12	20	14
12						26
40		53				
14				26		
50	60					
11			41			
13					33	

–	25	29	20	26	28
10			10		
13				13	
11	14				
14					14
12		17			

2. Work out the answers to these problems.

a. Find the total of forty and eleven. ☐

b. Twenty-seven take away thirteen. ☐

c. Take a quarter from a half. ☐

d. Work out the value of thirty-seven and thirty. ☐

3. Write the missing numbers in the empty spaces.

a. 39 – 7 = _____

b. 15 + _____ = 19

c. 21 + _____ = 29

d. _____ – 6 = 21

e. _____ – 5 = 13

f. 12 + 6 = _____

 Draw an add chart like the one in part 1. Write in different numbers along the top and down the side, then fill in the squares.

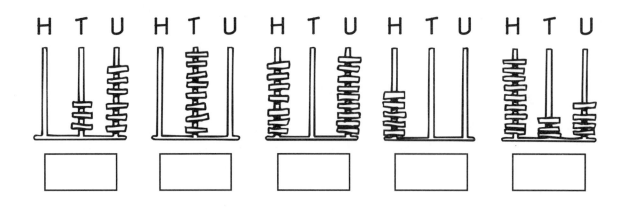

PLACE VALUE WHEN ADDING AND SUBTRACTING

1. How much does each abacus show?

H T U   H T U   H T U   H T U   H T U

2a. Add 10 to these numbers.

3		7		14		38		569	

b. Now subtract 10 from these amounts.

17		34		58		42		29	

3. Give the answers to these questions.

a.   How many times greater than 1p is 10p?

b.   How many times less than 100cm is 10cm?

c.   How many times greater than 1m is 100m?

d.   How many times less than 10g is 1g?

Draw ten abacuses and show different HTU amounts.

P

QUICK MENTAL MATHS

ADDING AND SUBTRACTING SEVERAL NUMBERS

1. Add these amounts together.

Subtract the two smaller numbers from the larger one.

a. 1p, 12p, 3p

f. 12, 3, 2

b. 2kg, 14kg, 4kg

g. 15, 4, 5

c. 11m, 5m, 3m

h. 20, 5, 5

d. 2g, 2g, 13g

i. 6, 4, 18

e. 10cm, 3cm, 5cm

j. 3, 25, 7

2. Work out the answers to these word problems.

a. To seven, add two and eleven.

b. From seventeen, subtract two and three.

c. Add the even numbers together: 6, 9, 4, 8, 7, 5

d. Total up 3, 7 and 6. Take your answer from twenty.

3. Write in the answers to these problems.

a. $12 + 25 + 5 =$ _____

c. $19 + 15 + 5 =$ _____

b. $18 - 3 - 10 =$ _____

d. $16 - 6 - 7 =$ _____

Make up your own addition and subtraction sums using three or four numbers.

QUICK MENTAL MATHS

TEST YOUR SKILLS 1 (B1–B6)

B1 Write down eight pairs of numbers that add up to 16.

a. _____   c. _____   e. _____   g. _____

b. _____   d. _____   f. _____   h. _____

B2 **a.** Write down all the odd numbers between 10 and 20.

_____

b. Subtract each of these odd numbers from 20.

_____

B3 Write in the missing number sentence.

20 = 12 + 8, 20 = 8 + 12, 20 − 8 = 12, _____

B4 Make these numbers twice the size.

| 400 | | 250 | | 300 | | 450 | |

B5 Make up six add sums which have answers less than 20. Write them with the largest number first.

a. _____   c. _____   e. _____

b. _____   d. _____   f. _____

B6 Do these add and take away problems by looking for doubles.

| a. | 22 | + | 20 | = | | c. | 16 | − | 7 | = | |
| b. | 10 | + | 12 | = | | d. | 12 | − | 5 | = | |

QUICK MENTAL MATHS

TOTAL

TEST YOUR SKILLS 2 (B7–B12)

B7 Complete these number patterns.

a. 7 – 3 = 4, 17 – 3 = ____ 27 – 3 = ____ 37 – 3 = ___

b. 5 + 4 = 9, 15 + 4 = ____ 25 + 4 = ____ 35 + 4 = ___

c. 9 – 5 = 4, 19 – 5 = ____ 29 – 5 = ____ 39 – 5 = ___

B8 Break these sums into tens and ones.

a. (9cm) + (17cm) = [　　　 tens] and [　　　 ones]

b. (7kg) + (28kg) = [　　　 tens] and [　　　 ones]

B9 Work out the answer to this problem.

15 – 7 = 15 – 5 – 2 = 10 – 2 = [　　　　]

B10 Read this question carefully and write the answer in the box.

What is twenty-six add thirteen? [　　　]

B11 Add 10 and then subtract 10 from these amounts.

a.
17	+10	–10

b.
41	+10	–10

B12 Work out the answer to this number sentence.

Twenty take away 6 subtract 8. _____

TOTAL

MULTIPLICATION FACTS

MULTIPLICATION AND DIVISION

1. Fill in the missing amounts.

a. $2 \times 5\text{kg} = \boxed{}$

f. $4\text{m} \times \boxed{} = 40\text{m}$

b. $6 \times \boxed{} = 12\text{p}$

g. $\boxed{} \times 5 = 40\text{kg}$

c. $\boxed{} \times 10 = 70\text{cm}$

h. $7\text{p} \times 2 = \boxed{}$

d. $6\text{p} \times \boxed{} = 30\text{p}$

i. $5 \times \boxed{} = 50\text{cm}$

e. $4 \times 2\text{m} = \boxed{}$

j. $\boxed{} \times 5\text{g} = 15\text{g}$

2. Find the answers to these questions.

a. Nine groups of 5. How many altogether? _____

b. Eight times two gives what number? _____

c. What number is ten times more than two? _____

d. How many is 10×3? _____   e. Twice 5 equals? _____

3. Complete this chart.

×	0	1	2	3	4	5	6	7	8	9	10
2										18	
10						50					

✏ Start at $1 \times 5 = 5$ and write out the 5 times table.
See if you can get as far as $20 \times 5 = 100$, or even further!

QUICK MENTAL MATHS

DIVISION FACTS

1. Fill in the missing amounts.

a. 12kg ÷ 2 = ☐

f. 20m ÷ ☐ = 10m

b. 30p ÷ ☐ = 3p

g. ☐ ÷ 10 = 9kg

c. ☐ ÷ 10 = 6cm

h. 18p ÷ 2 = ☐

d. 14p ÷ ☐ = 7p

i. 10cm ÷ ☐ = 5cm

e. 4m × 10 = ☐

j. ☐ ÷ 2 = 8g

2. Draw these items in batches of 2, then write in the boxes how many groups there are.

a. 14 tennis balls ☐ ☐

b. 10 fish ☐ ☐

3. How many:

a. Twos in 8? _____

d. Tens in 90? _____

b. Tens in forty? _____

e. 2s in eighteen? _____

c. 2s in six? _____

f. 10s in seventy? _____

Start at 5 ÷ 5 = 1, 10 ÷ 5 = 2... Carry on and see how far you can get. Can you reach 150 ÷ 5 = 30?

MULTIPLICATION AND DIVISION

NAME _____ CLASS _____

RELATIONSHIP BETWEEN × AND ÷

MULTIPLICATION AND DIVISION

1. Find the missing numbers.

a. 6 × 10cm = ☐

☐ × 6cm = 60cm

60cm ÷ ☐ = 6cm

60cm ÷ 6 = ☐

b. 35p ÷ 5 = ☐

☐ ÷ 7 = 5p

7p × ☐ = 35p

5p × 7 = ☐

2. Fill in the blanks.

a. You know that 8 × 10 = _____ What is 80 ÷ 10? _____

b. You know that 7 × 2 = _____ What is 14 ÷ 2? _____

c. You know that 6 × 5 = _____ What is 30 ÷ 5? _____

d. You know that 25 × 3 = _____ What is 75 ÷ 3? _____

e. You know that 9 × 5 = _____ What is 45 ÷ 5? _____

3. Write out four facts using the digits 4, 2 and 8. Looking at part 1 will help you. The first fact has been done for you.

_____ 4 × 2 = 8 _____   _____

_____   _____

Make up your own sets of four facts using three numbers like the two sets shown at the top of the page. Use your 2, 5 and 10 times tables.

QUICK MENTAL MATHS

DOUBLES AND HALVES

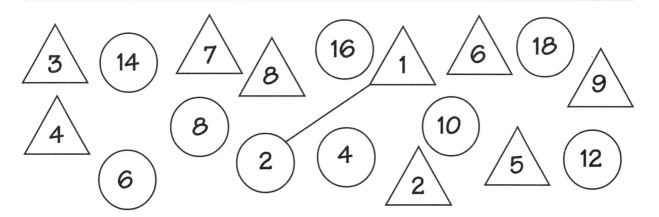

1a. Join each number in a triangle to its double in a circle.

b. Now shade each pair of joined up shapes in the same colour.

2. Put half of each amount in the left-hand box and double it in the right-hand box. The first one has been done for you.

a.	5p	10p	20p

b.		20m	

c.		30cm	

d.		40kg	

e.		50g	

f.		60g	

g.		70kg	

h.		80cm	

i.		90m	

j.		£ 1	

3. Answer this question in one word.

Joe has 8 pens and Clare twice as many.
How many does Clare have?

Double the numbers between 20 and 30. Halve the even numbers between 40 and 50.

QUICK MENTAL MATHS

MULTIPLICATION AND DIVISION

MULTIPLICATION ORDER

1. Below each multiplication fact, write another one which gives the same answer. The first one has been done for you.

a. $3 \times 2 = 6$
$2 \times 3 = 6$

b. $2 \times 1 = 2$
_____

c. $4 \times 2 = 8$
_____

d. $2 \times 5 = 10$
_____

e. $5 \times 3 = 15$
_____

f. $5 \times 7 = 35$
_____

g. $2 \times 7 = 14$
_____

h. $9 \times 5 = 45$
_____

i. $2 \times 9 = 18$
_____

2a. Solve this money problem.

Five 2p coins have the same value as _____ coins.

b. Show this fact in the form of two drawings and two multiplication facts.

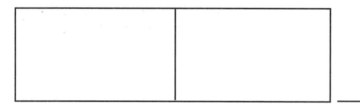

_____ _____

3. Circle the multiplication that is equal to the one in the triangle.

3×2 4×1 3×3 6×0

0×6 2×3 2×2

 Using the 5 and 10 times tables, write out some more pairs of multiplication facts like those in part 1.

DIVISION WITH REMAINDERS

1. Fill in these charts. Write the division in the top row and the remainder underneath. Some numbers are in already.

÷	21	76	42	58	69
10	2		4		
r	1	6		8	

÷	7	11	24	18	27
5		2		3	
r	2		4		2

2. Answer these questions carefully.

a. How many 2cm lengths of string can be cut from a

9cm length? _____

What length of string is left over? _____

b. John had 15p and spent 12p. How much money did

he have left? _____

c. What is the remainder when 35 is shared by 10? _____

3. Write in the answers and how many there are left over.

a. 19 ÷ 2 = [   ] r [   ] **d.** 26 ÷ 5 = [   ] r [   ]

b. 38 ÷ 5 = [   ] r [   ] **e.** 37 ÷ 10 = [   ] r [   ]

c. 43 ÷ 10 = [   ] r [   ] **f.** 13 ÷ 2 = [   ] r [   ]

 Make up some more divisions that have 'remainders'.

MULTIPLICATION AND DIVISION

CALCULATION PATTERNS (× AND ÷)

1. Find the missing numbers in these patterns.

a. 1 × 2 = _____

3 × _____ = 6

_____ × 2 = 10

7 × 2 = _____

9 × _____ = 18

b. 50 ÷ 10 = _____

60 ÷ _____ = 6

_____ ÷ 10 = 7

80 ÷ 10 = _____

90 ÷ _____ = 9

2. What do you notice about the pattern of the numbers above?

_____

_____

3. Cross out the numbers that are NOT answers to the 5 times table. One has been done for you.

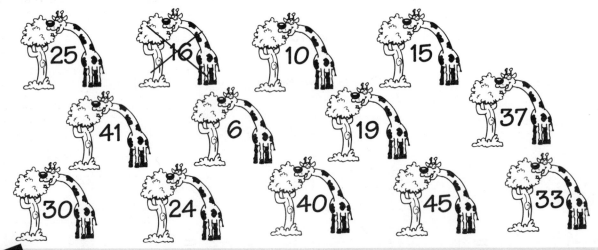

Explain how you knew which of the numbers above were not answers to the 5 times table.

MULTIPLYING BY 1, 10

1. Join each single-digit number to a number 10 times the size.

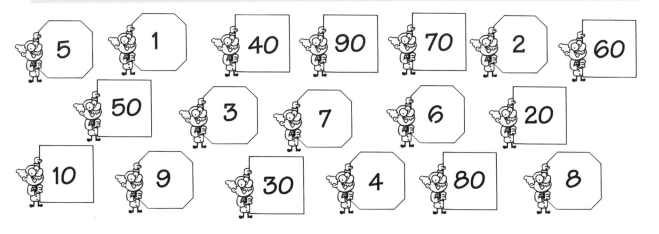

5   1   40   90   70   2   60

50   3   7   6   20

10   9   30   4   80   8

2. What happens to a number when you multiply it by 1?

_____

_____

3. Make each number 10 times smaller and then 10 times larger. The first one has been done for you.

	÷10		×10			÷10		×10
a.	1	10	100	f.		60	
b.		70		g.		50	
c.		20		h.		30	
d.		90		i.		80	
e.		40		j.		5	

Make the single-digit numbers in part 1 a hundred times bigger. Write them out in order of size, starting with the smallest.

QUICK MENTAL MATHS

MULTIPLICATION AND DIVISION

DIVIDING BY 1, 10

1. Make each number 10 times smaller.
The first one has been done for you.

a. | 60 | 6 | | 30 | | | 50 | | | 10 | |

b. | 80 | | | 100 | | | 20 | | | 40 | |

Divide these amounts by ten. The first one has been done for you.

c. | 70p | 7p | | 90p | | | 200p | | | 400p | |

2. Mark on each abacus a number that is 10 times smaller than the number in the shape underneath it.

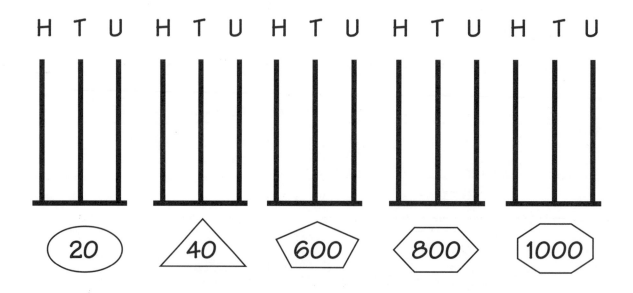

H T U   H T U   H T U   H T U   H T U

20   40   600   800   1000

3. Carefully answer this question.

What is a tenth of three hundred?

 Choose five numbers of your own and show them 10 times smaller. Like this: 900 — 90 or 2000 — 200.

MORE MULTIPLICATION FACTS

1. Circle the multiplications in each box that have the same answer as the number on the left.

a.	4 × 0
	3 × 10
40	10 × 4
	2 × 20
	4 × 5

b.	2 × 10
	0 × 2
20	2 × 5
	8 × 2
	1 × 20

c.	10 × 5
	20 × 3
60	4 × 20
	2 × 30
	6 × 2

2. Read these problems and work them out.

a. How many fives make seventy?_____

b. Four groups of 20 are equal to how *altogether?* many?_____

c. How many ones are there in 8 sets of 2?_____

d. Multiply 6 groups of 5 by two. _____

3. Write a multiplication fact for these addition sums.

a. 2 + 2 + 2 + 2 + 2 + 2 + 2 + 2 + 2 ___9 × ___

b. 5 + 5 + 5 + 5 + 5 + 5 + 5 + 5 _____ × 5

c. 10 + 10 + 10 + 10 + 10 + 10 + 10 ___ × ___

Make up some multiplications like those in part 1 and test your friends.

C11

MULTIPLICATION AND DIVISION

PLACE VALUE WHEN MULTIPLYING AND DIVIDING

1. Look at the amounts shown in each abacus and then write a table fact for that amount. The first one has been done for you.

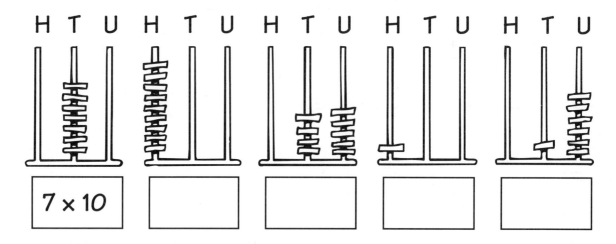

7 × 10				

2. Now draw some abacuses to show the amounts below.

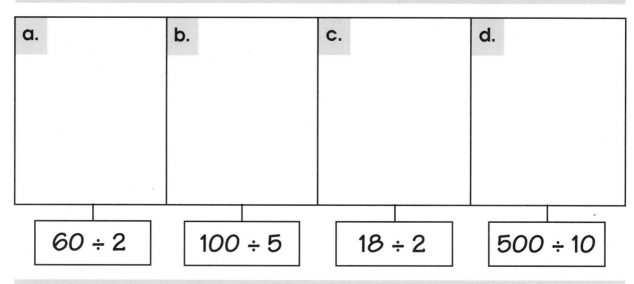

a. | b. | c. | d.

| 60 ÷ 2 | 100 ÷ 5 | 18 ÷ 2 | 500 ÷ 10 |

3. Fill in the missing numbers.

a. **5 times 30 is the same as___hundred and____tens.**

b. **250 shared by 10 is the same as___tens and__units.**

Write down ten different numbers. Make each number 10 times the size and then 100 times the size.

× AND ÷ WHOLE NUMBERS AND FRACTIONS

1a. Multiply these numbers by 2.

30	90	60	50	20	70	100

b. Divide these numbers by 5.

50	300	450	200	350	500	150

2. Put the missing amounts in the boxes.

a. 2 × 2kg = ☐

b. 40p ÷ ☐ = 8p

c. ☐ × 10 = 60cm

d. 16p ÷ ☐ = 8p

e. 7 × 5m = ☐

f. 18m ÷ ☐ = 9m

g. ☐ × 4 = 40kg

h. 80p ÷ 10 = ☐

i. 5 × ☐ = 25cm

j. ☐ ÷ 5 = 10g

3. Fill in the blank spaces.

a. 10 halves is the same as _____ whole ones.

b. How many ½ litres of milk in 2 litres? _____

Write the fraction pattern for ½ like this: ½, 1, 1½… up to 20.

MULTIPLICATION AND DIVISION

C13

TEST YOUR SKILLS 1 (C1–C6)

MULTIPLICATION AND DIVISION

C1   Complete this chart.

×2	2		6						20
×5		10				30		45	
×10			30				80		

C2   Write how many 2s, 5s and 10s there are in the following numbers.

	2s	5s	10s
a.	10		
b.	30		

	2s	5s	10s
c.	40		
d.	50		

	2s	5s	10s
e.	60		
f.	20		

C3   Put in the missing numbers.

You know that 8p × 5 = _____ What is 40p ÷ 5? _____

C4   Halve and double these amounts.

a.	6p	12p	24p

c.		£1.20	

b.		14m	

d.			140g

C5   Change the order of these multiplication facts to give the same answer.

a.   Seven × two = 14   b.   Eight × five = 40

_____   _____

C6   Write in the answers and how many there are left over.

a.   15 ÷ 2 = _____ r _____   b.   28 ÷ 5 = _____ r _____

QUICK MENTAL MATHS

TOTAL

TEST YOUR SKILLS 2 (C7–C12)

C7 a. Cross out the numbers that are not in the 2 times table.

3   18   12   19   6   15   14   11   16   20

b. Cross out the numbers that are not in the 10 times table.

80   20   25   74   88   30   100   99   50

C8 Make these numbers 10 times smaller and 10 times larger.

	÷10		×10			÷10		×10
a.		100			c.		150	
b.		700			d.		230	

C9 Work out this word problem.

Make 2 x 50 ten times smaller. [ ]

C10 Write a multiplication fact for these addition sums.

a. 5 + 5 + 5 _____   b. 2 + 2 + 2 + 2 + 2 _____

C11 Fill in the missing numbers.

a. 5 times 80 equals____hundreds and____tens.

b. 55 shared by 5 equals____ten and____unit.

C12 Choose the correct word from the two that are given.

8 [ ] are the same as 4. (quarters, halves)

MULTIPLICATION AND DIVISION

TOTAL

MULTISTEP AND MIXED OPERATIONS

D1

ADDING AND SUBTRACTING

1. Fill in the missing amounts.

a. $2 + 3 + 4 + 2 = \underline{}$

f. $20 - 10 - \underline{} = 5$

b. $15 - 4 - \underline{} = 6$

g. $18 - \underline{} - 7 = 5$

c. $\underline{} + 6 + 1 + 8 = 20$

h. $30 + 20 + \underline{} = 80$

d. $17 - 7 - 7 = \underline{}$

i. $60 - 20 - 5 = \underline{}$

e. $9 + 3 + 4 = \underline{}$

j. $\underline{} + 7 + 5 = 19$

2. Read these questions carefully and answer them.

a. Twelve plus three plus five is how many?_____

b. Ten add six plus five?_____

c. 17 minus 8 take away 3 leaves how many?_____

d. What is the total of 4cm, 7cm, 5cm and 2cm?_____

3. Total up these numbers and then add ten to your answer.

a.

5p	8p	7p	

b.

3kg	7kg	5kg	

c.

15cm	10cm	5cm	

d.

9g	6g	30g	

Make up some number sentences like the ones at the top of this sheet, using the plus and minus signs.

MULTIPLYING AND DIVIDING

1 Make the answers to these problems twice as big. There are two stages to finding the right answer. Be careful! The first answer has been done for you.

a. $6 \div 2$ | 6 | 8×5 | | $35 \div 5$ | | 9×10 | |

Make the answers to these sums 10 times larger. The first one has been done for you.

b. $8 \div 2$ | 40 | 4×5 | | $10 \div 2$ | | 10×8 | |

c. 9×5 | | 5×2 | | $25 \div 5$ | | 2×10 | |

2. Fill in the answers.

a. _____ $= 2 \times 5 \times 10$

b. $3 \times 2 \times 10 =$ _____

c. $4 \times 10 \times 2 =$ _____

d. $20 \div 2 \div 2 =$ _____

e. $40 \div 10 \div 2 =$ _____

f. $30 \div 5 \div 2 =$ _____

3. Work out this problem.

There are 10 cakes in a packet. Carol buys 2 packets and shares the cakes between 5 children.

How many cakes will each child get?_____

Make up some more sums using three numbers like the ones in part 2 of this sheet.

ADDING AND MULTIPLYING

1. Fill in the table below. The first one has been done for you.

a.	2 + 2 + 2 + 2	4 × 2	8
b.	5 + 5 + 5 + 5 + 5		
c.		6 × 10	
d.		3 × 20	
e.	5 + 5 + 5 + 5 + 5 + 5 + 5		

2. Join each number to the number sentences that belong to it.

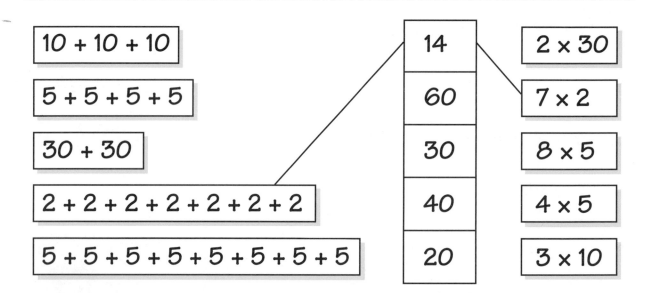

10 + 10 + 10		14		2 × 30
5 + 5 + 5 + 5		60		7 × 2
30 + 30		30		8 × 5
2 + 2 + 2 + 2 + 2 + 2 + 2		40		4 × 5
5 + 5 + 5 + 5 + 5 + 5 + 5 + 5		20		3 × 10

3. Write in the answers.

a. _____ = (2 × 8) + 73

b. (25 + 25) × 2 = _____

 Write out the 3 times table and next to each sum put the add sum that means the same. Try with the 4 times table if you have time.

SUBTRACTING AND DIVIDING

1. Work out the answers to these problems.

a. $19 - 3 - 6 =$ _____   f. $18 - 4 - 4 =$ _____

b. $60 \div 10 \div 2 =$ _____   g. $50 \div 10 \div 5 =$ _____

c. $20 \div 5 \div 2 =$ _____   h. $16 - 7 - 2 =$ _____

d. $40 \div 5 \div 2 =$ _____   i. $30 \div 10 \div 1 =$ _____

e. $15 - 5 - 3 =$ _____   j. $17 - 6 - 5 =$ _____

2. Try to do the following number problems.

a. Subtract six and seven from 18. _____

b. There are 5 marbles in each bag. There are 6 bags. Tim takes away 2 bags. How many marbles are left? _____

c. Divide 30 by 5 and take away 4. _____

3. Halve the number on the left and take your answer away from 50.

a.

20	40	80		10		30	

b.

40		50		60		70	

✏️ Draw some more boxes like the ones above. Put in your own numbers on the left. Halve each number and subtract the answer from 100.

A1

1. **a.** 8p, **10p**, 12p, **14p**, 16p, **18p**, 20p, 22p, **24p**
b. 30, **27**, **24**, 21, 18, **15**, 12, **9**, 6

2. **a.** Squares – 8, 12, 16, 20, 24, 28 – all coloured red.
b. Squares - 10, 15, 20, 25, 30, 35, 40 – all coloured blue.

3. **zero**, ten, **twenty**, thirty, **forty**, fifty, sixty, seventy, **eighty**, ninety, **one hundred**

A2

1. **a.** 20 **b.** 8 **c.** 55 **d.** 30 **e.** 1
f. 40 **g.** 33 **h.** 19 **i.** 40 **j.** 7

2. **a.** 5, 4 **b.** 6, 7 **c.** 7, 2

3. **a.** 3 **b.** 70 **c.** 100

A3

1. **a.** 14kg, 22kg, 31kg, 43kg, 45kg, 50kg
b. 49cm, 41cm, 33cm, 20cm, 17cm, 16cm

2. **a.** **23 25 28,** 36 38 41, 29 31 34
b. 17 19 22, 42 44 47, 25 27 30
c. 9 11 14, 6 8 11, 38 40 43

3. **a.** ☐☐ **b.** ☐☐☐ **c.** ☐☐

A4

1. Bear: 2–4, Dog:7–9, Camel: 9–11, Pig: 11–13

2. The 11m plank should be ticked.
The 11m plank should be red.
The 7m plank should be blue.
The 9m plank should be green.

3. Open-ended

A5

1. 10cm, 100cm, 30cm, 50cm, 40cm, 70cm.

2. **a.** **38, 40 b.** 11, 10 **c.** 68, 70
d. 21, 20 **e.** 18, 20 **f.** 33, 30
g. 30, 30 **h.** 45, 50 **i.** 43, 40
j. 31, 30

3. **a.** **70 b.** 40 **c.** 50p
d. 9 o'clock

A6

A1. **a.** **12p**, **15p**, 18p, **21p**, 24p, **27p**, 30p
b. 28m, **24m**, 20m, **16m**, 12m, **8m**, 4m

A2. **a.** 4 **b.** 20 **c.** 100
d. 30 **e.** 7 **f.** 40 **g.** 53

A3. **a.** ☐☐ **b.** ☐☐

c. 14kg, 27kg, 36kg, 49kg, 53kg

A7

A4. **a.** Answers between the following amounts are acceptable: 19 (17–22) 51 (49–53) 82 (80–84) 48 (46–50) 97 (95–99)
b. Answers between the following amounts are acceptable 95–99, 55–59, 30–34
c. a:1–3 b: 4–6 c:7 d: 10–12

A5. **a.** 38, 40 **b.** 23, 20 **c.** 15, 20
d. 13, 10 **e.** 17, 20 **f.** 18, 20 **g.** 9 o'clock

B1

1. a. 10kg b. 6p c. 16cm d. 12p e. 18m f. 4p g. 6cm h. 8m i. 4kg j. 3g
2. a. 11, 17, 12, 14 b. 15, 8, 16, 19 c. 18, 2, 13, 6
3. a. 7 b. 11

B2

1.

9	–	0	=	9
9	–	1	=	8
9	–	2	=	7
9	–	3	=	6
9	–	4	=	5

9	–	9	=	0
9	–	8	=	1
9	–	7	=	2
9	–	6	=	3
9	–	5	=	4

2. Sums open-ended.
3. a. 7 b. 10 c. 7 d. 12

B3

1. a. 19cm, 5cm, 14cm, 14cm
   b. 18p, 7p, 11p, 11p
   c. Open-ended – but an answer that points out that the same three amounts are used in all four sums is satisfactory.
2. a. 29m, 12m, 12m, 12m
   b. 80g, 50g, 30g, 30g
3. 28 – 13 = 15

B4

1. a. 7 + 1, 6 + 2, 5 + 3, 4 + 4, 0 + 8
   b. 9 + 1, 8 + 2, 7 + 3, 6 + 4, 5 + 5, 0 + 10
2. a. 18, 20, 22, 24
   b. 26, 28, 30, 40
   c. 50, 60, 80, 100
3. a. sixteen pence b. fourteen pence c. ten

B5

1. a. 13 + 5 = 18 b. 11 + 8 = 19
   c. 16 + 3 = 19 d. 12 + 7 = 19
   e. 14 + 4 = 18 f. 17 + 3 = 20
   g. 12 + 5 = 17 h. 14 + 6 = 20
   i. 11 + 6 = 17 j. 15 + 3 = 18
2. Open-ended – six addition sums using all the numbers given (check that the largest number has been written first).
3. 14, 16, 21, 27

B6

1. a. 13 b. 17 c. 25 d. 31 e. 39 f. 29 g. 23 h. 35 i. 21 j. 19
2. a. 5 b. 6 – 3 + 1 c. 7 d. 6 e. 40 – 20 – 1 f. 7
3. a. 81 b. 59 c. 51 d. 8

B7

1.

12	13	14	15	16
13	14	15	16	17
14	15	16	17	18
15	16	17	18	19
16	17	18	19	20

a. 16 b. 9 c. 8 d. 16 e. 6
2. a. All the same numbers in the square should be shaded in the same colour.
   b. Open-ended – accept any sensible answer.
3. a. 13, 23, 63 b. 17, 27, 87 c. 15, 45, 95

B8

1. a. 16 + 8 = 15 + 1 + 5 + 3 = 15 + 5 + 1 + 3 = 20 + 4 = 24
   b. 17 + 8 = 15 + 2 + 5 + 3 = 15 + 5 + 2 + 3 = 20 + 5 = 25
2. a. 26kg b. 23p c. 26cm d. 23p e. 25m f. 34cm g. 36m h. 35kg i. 37p j. 33p
3. thirty-five

B9

1. **a.** 15 **b.** 17 **c.** 15 **d.** 14 **e.** 11 **f.** 11
   g. 13 **h.** 13 **i.** 12 **j.** 16

2. **a.** 6 **b.** 8 **c.** 7 **d.** 7 **e.** 7 **f.** 10 **g.** 9

3. **a.** 25 **b.** 20 − 5 = 15
   c. 25 − 5 − 4 = 20 − 4 = 16

B10

1.

22	25	42	24	32	26
50	53	70	52	60	54
24	27	44	26	34	28
60	63	80	62	70	64
21	24	41	23	31	25
23	26	43	25	33	27

15	19	10	16	18
12	16	7	13	15
14	18	9	15	17
11	15	6	12	14
13	17	8	14	16

2. **a.** 51 **b.** 14 **c.** ¼ **d.** 67

3. **a.** 32 **b.** 4 **c.** 8 **d.** 27 **e.** 18 **f.** 18

B11

1. 36, 80, 709, 500, 934

2. **a.** 13, 17, 24, 48, 579
   b. 7, 24, 48, 32, 19

3. **a.** 10 **b.** 10 **c.** 100 **d.** 10

B12

1. **a.** 16p **b.** 20kg **c.** 19m **d.** 17g
   e. 18cm
   f. 7 **g.** 6 **h.** 10 **i.** 8 **j.** 15

2. **a.** 20 **b.** 12 **c.** 18 **d.** 4

3. **a.** 42 **b.** 5 **c.** 39 **d.** 3

B13

B1. 1 + 15, 2 + 14, 3 + 13, 4 + 12,
5 + 11, 6 + 10, 7 + 9, 8 + 8

B2. **a.** 11, 13, 15, 17, 19
b. 20 − 11 = 9, 20 − 13 = 7, 20 − 15 = 5
20 − 17 = 3, 20 − 19 = 1

B3. 20 − 12 = 8

B4. 800 500 600 900

B5. Open-ended – six addition sums with answers less than 20.

B6. **a.** 42 **b.** 22 **c.** 9 **d.** 7

B14

B7. **a.** **4**, 14, 24, 34 **b.** **9**, 19, 29, 39
c. **4**, 14, 24, 34

B8. **a.** 2 tens and 6 ones
b. 3 tens and 5 ones

B9. 8

B10. 39

B11. **a.** 27, 7 **b.** 51, 31

B12. 6

C1

1. **a.** 10kg **b.** 2p **c.** 7cm **d.** 5 **e.** 8m
   f. 10 **g.** 8kg **h.** 14p **i.** 10cm **j.** 3

2. **a.** 45 **b.** 16 **c.** 20 **d.** 30 **e.** 10

3.

0	2	4	6	8	10	12	14	16	18	20
0	10	20	30	40	50	60	70	80	90	100

C2

1. **a.** 6kg **b.** 10 **c.** 60cm **d.** 2
   e. 40m **f.** 2 **g.** 90kg **h.** 9p **i.** 2
   j. 16g

2. **a.** seven groups of two tennis balls, 7
   b. five groups of two fish, 5

3. **a.** 4 **b.** 4 **c.** 3 **d.** 9 **e.** 9 **f.** 7

1. a. 60cm, 10, 10, 10cm
b. 7p, 35p, 5, 35p ⟨C3⟩

2. a. 80, 8 b. 14, 7 c. 30, 6 d. 75, 25
e. 45, 9

3. **4 × 2 = 8**, 2 × 4 = 8,
8 ÷ 2 = 4, 8 ÷ 4 = 2

---

1. a. **(1–2)** (2–4) (3–6) (4–8) ⟨C4⟩
(5–10) (6–12) (7–14) (8–16)
(9–18)
b. Each pair of joined up shapes
should be the same colour.

2. a. **5p, 20p** b. 10m, 40m c. 15cm, 60cm
d. 20kg, 80kg e. 25g, 100g f. 30g, 120g
g. 35kg, 140kg h. 40cm, 160cm
i. 45m, 180m j. 50p, £2 (200p)

3. Sixteen

---

1. a. **2 × 3 = 6** b. 1 × 2 = 2 ⟨C5⟩
c. 2 × 4 = 8 d. 5 × 2 = 10
e. 3 × 5 = 15 f. 7 × 5 = 35
g. 7 × 2 = 14 h. 5 × 9 = 45
i. 9 × 2 = 18

2. a. 2 b. Drawing to show five 2p coins
and two 5p coins.
5 × 2p = 10p, 2 × 5p = 10p

3. Box with 3 × 2 should be circled.

---

1.  ⟨C6⟩

2. a. 4 lengths, 1 cm left over b. 3p c. 5

3. a. 9 r 1 b. 7 r 3 c. 4 r 3 d. 5 r 1
e. 3 r 7 f. 6 r 1

---

1. a. 2, 2, 5, 14, 2
b. 5, 10, 70, 8, 10 ⟨C7⟩

2. Open-ended – accept any sensible
answers – such as the various number
patterns for each column of numbers.

3. These numbers should be crossed out:
16, 6, 19, 24, 33, 37, 41

---

1. (1–10) (2–20) (3–30) (4–40) (5–50) ⟨C8⟩
(6–60) (7–70) (8–80) (9–90)

2. The number stays the same.

3. a. **1, 100** b. 7, 700 c. 2, 200 d. 9, 900
e. 4, 400 f. 6, 600 g. 5, 500 h. 3, 300
i. 8, 800 j. ½, 50

---

1. a. **6, 3, 5, 1** b. 8, 10, 2, 4 c. 7p, ⟨C9⟩
9p, 20p, 40p

2.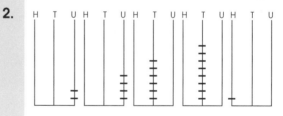

3. 30

---

1. Circled: a. 10 × 4, 2 × 20 ⟨C10⟩
b. 2 × 10, 1 × 20 c. 20 × 3,
2 × 30

2. a. 14 b. 80 c. 16 d. 60

3. a. 9 × 2 = 18 b. 8 × 5 = 40
c. 7 × 10 = 70

C11		**D1**

C11

1. Open-ended – but most likely answers are: 9 × 100, 9 × 5, 10 × 10, 8 × 2

2.

3. **a.** 1 hundred and 5 tens
   b. 2 tens and 5 units

D1

1. **a.** 11 **b.** 5 **c.** 5 **d.** 3 **e.** 16 **f.** 5 **g.** 6 **h.** 30 **i.** 35 **j.** 7

2. **a.** 20 **b.** 21 **c.** 6 **d.** 18cm

3. **a.** 30p **b.** 25kg **c.** 40cm **d.** 55g

C12

1. **a.** 60, 180, 120, 100, 40, 140, 200
   b. 10, 60, 90, 40, 70, 100, 30

2. **a.** 4kg **b.** 5 **c.** 6cm **d.** 2 **e.** 35m **f.** 2 **g.** 10kg **h.** 8p **i.** 5cm **j.** 50g

3. **a.** 5 **b.** 4

D2

1. **a.** 6, 80, 14, 180 **b.** 40, 200, 50, 800, 450, 100, 50, 200

2. **a.** 100 **b.** 60 **c.** 80 **d.** 5 **e.** 2 **f.** 3

3. 4 cakes

C13

C1.

2	4	6	8	10	12	14	16	18	20
5	10	15	20	25	30	35	40	45	50
10	20	30	40	50	60	70	80	90	100

C2. **a.** 5, 2, 1 **b.** 15, 6, 3 **c.** 20, 8, 4 **d.** 25, 10, 5 **e.** 30, 12, 6 **f.** 10, 4, 2

C3. 40p, 8p

C4. **a. 6p, 24p b.** 7m, 28m **c.** 60p, £2.40 **d.** 70g, 280g

C5. **a.** two × seven = 14
   b. five × eight = 40

C6. **a.** 7 r 1 **b.** 5 r 3

D3

1. **a. 4 × 2, 8 b.** 5 × 5, 25
   c. 10 + 10 + 10 + 10 + 10 + 10, 60 **d.** 20 + 20 + 20, 60 **e.** 7 × 5, 35

2. Check that the centre numbers are joined correctly to both the addition and multiplication sums.

3. **a.** 89 **b.** 100

C14

C7. **a.** The following numbers should be crossed out: 3, 19, 15, 11
   b. The following numbers should be crossed out: 25, 74, 88, 99

C8. **a.** 10, 1000 **b.** 70, 7000 **c.** 15, 1500 **d.** 23, 2300

C9. 10

C10. **a.** 3 × 5 = 15 **b.** 5 × 2 = 10

C11. **a.** 4 hundreds and 0 tens
    b. 1 ten and 1 unit

C12 halves

D4

1. **a.** 10 **b.** 3 **c.** 2 **d.** 4 **e.** 7 **f.** 10 **g.** 1 **h.** 7 **i.** 3 **j.** 6

2. **a.** 5 **b.** 20 marbles **c.** 2

3. **a. 40**, 10, 45, 35 **b.** 30, 25, 20, 15